BOOK 3

Learn to Read with

Janet and John

Friends

Published by
Star Kids Ltd.,
10 Greycoat Place,
London SW1P 1SB

Authors: Penny Coltman, Jayne Greenwood and Val Mitchell

Illustrations: Colin Bowler

Liz Pichon (pages 10,11,12, 20, 21, 22).

Prepared by Tandem Design, Southampton.

First published 2001

© Star Kids 2001

A CIP record for this book is available from the British Library.

ISBN 1 84258 0566

Printed in Spain

Ako's Visit

Ako is from Japan.
Ako came to stay.

Ako had some paper.

She could make a bird.

Ako had some chopsticks.

She could eat with them.

Ako played with Tim.

Then Ako went home.

What do friends do?

play

share

give

wave

help

hug

fall out ...

... and make up.

Mr Green's Illness

Mr and Mrs Green live next
door to Janet and John.
They are all friends.

Mr Green was ill.

"What could we do to help?"
said Janet and John.

"I could make him a card,"
said John.
"I could take a bunch of flowers,"
said Janet.

Janet and John went to see
Mr Green.
"How are you today?"
asked Janet.

"We have made you some
presents,"
said Janet and John.

"I am much better now,"
said Mr Green.
"You are good friends,"
said Mrs Green.

People who help us:

teacher

police officer

firefighter

lollipop man

vet

doctor

nurse

Family:

Mum   Dad   Gran   Tim

Janet and John Get Cross

Janet and John
were in the garden.

"I want the hoop," said Janet.
"No give it to me," said John.

Janet pulled the hoop.
John pulled the hoop.
They were cross.

"Stop that!" said Dad.
"Be friends," said Mum.

Janet fell down.
She hurt her leg.

John was upset.
"I am sorry," he said.
"I am sorry too," said Janet.

"Can we be friends?"

Key Word Reading

Below are listed the Key Words contained in this book.

Key Words are those that make up most of the
English language.

It is important that your child knows these words.
They are often repeated for emphasis, and used with
other phonic words - that is, words which can be
sounded out by children.

a	in
of	to
and	is
was	he
it	the
went	I
then	with

had	me
some	are
they	see
we	she
be	could
all	out
live	make
do	today
made	take
next	from
them	now

came	you
us	down
too	him
were	said

OXFORD
UNIVERSITY PRESS

Great Clarendon Street, Oxford, OX2 6DP, United Kingdom

Oxford University Press is a department of the University
of Oxford. It furthers the University's objective of excellence
in research, scholarship, and education by publishing
worldwide. Oxford is a registered trade mark of Oxford
University Press in the UK and in certain other countries

Text © Robin Etherington 2014

British Library Cataloguing in Publication Data
Data available

ISBN: 978-0-19-830819-5

10

Paper used in the production of this book is a natural, recyclable
product made from wood grown in sustainable forests. The
manufacturing process conforms to the environmental
regulations of the country of origin.

Printed in China by Golden Cup

Acknowledgements

Series Editor: Nikki Gamble
Illustrations: Zak Simmonds-Hurn

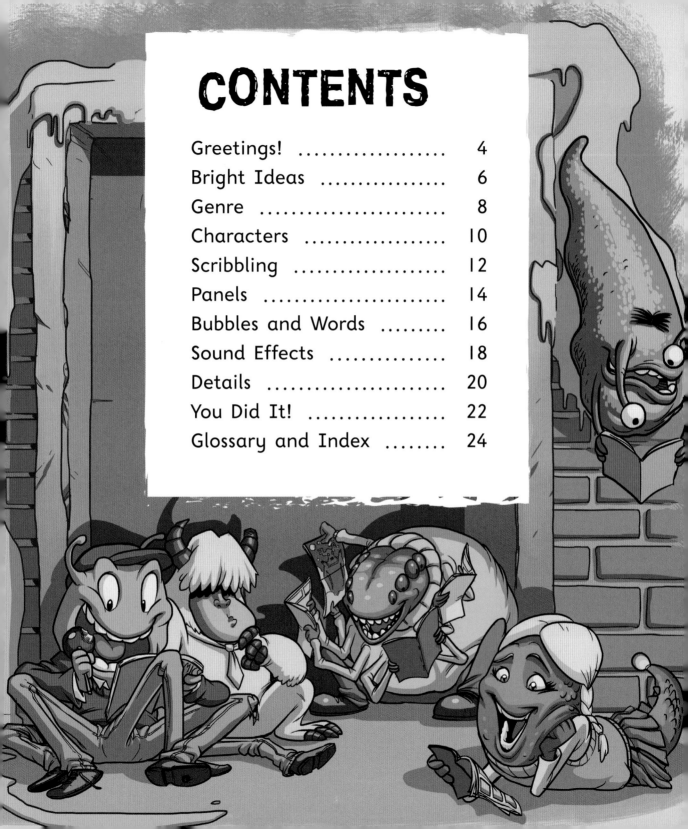

CONTENTS

CHAPTER 1:
GREETINGS!

Welcome to ... *Let's Make Comics!*
In this fun-packed book, we're going to share with you all the tips and tricks you need to make your own amazing comic stories.

My name is Robin. I write the words that go into a comic book.

Words like ...

BOOM!
KAPOW!
SMASH!

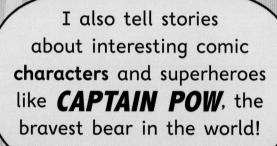

I also tell stories about interesting comic **characters** and superheroes like ***CAPTAIN POW***, the bravest bear in the world!

CHAPTER 2:
BRIGHT IDEAS

Before you begin to draw your comic, you need to think of an idea. Ideas eventually become stories.

Ideas don't have to be big ... and they don't have to be clever ...

Duh!

... but they should always be fun.

But where do ideas come from?

Both Robin and Zak keep a big box of ideas close to hand. Let's take a peek inside and see what ideas they've been collecting!

Good ideas for your own stories
can be found anywhere and any time:
1. inside books or comics
2. while playing a sport
3. when chatting to your friends
4. while playing with toys or games
5. on a day trip with your family.

... or perhaps
just something
completely silly!

Can you spot:
- a robot?
- a dragon?
- a skeleton?
- a rocket?

GOOD IDEAS

I've got it!
Aliens come to
Earth to steal all
our honey!

Turn for laughs
and scares ...

CHAPTER 3:
GENRE

Genre is a weird word. It's quite hard to say. It sounds a bit like saying *jon-ra*.

This tricky word is brilliant because it means the 'type of story' you want to tell.

COMEDY   HORROR

There are lots of different types of stories and deciding which one to use can be tough! If you're stuck, try and imagine a character from each different genre taking part in a running race.

The character who wins the race will decide what type of story you're going to tell ...

But who is going to win? Ready ... set ... GO!

CHAPTER 4:
CHARACTERS

A comic book is a bit like a movie or a cartoon.
You need characters to be your stars.

Yo.

Will they be human? Aliens? Robots?
Or perhaps an animal, like a cool bear
who also happens to be a superhero!

The choice is yours, but you don't have to think of your character straight away, because you can always start with ... stick people!

Stick people are fantastic at helping to build your comic. They're quick to create and fun to use.

Add a few props and your stick people can do all sorts of activities. Can you tell what jobs these stick people are doing?

Scribblers welcome in here ...

CHAPTER 5:
SCRIBBLING

Fact: Scribbling is great fun!

Comic creators like Robin and Zak always begin by scribbling, using just a pencil and a piece of paper.

Robin's private messy notebook!
This is where he plans all his comics.

Using stick people, he scribbles down his ideas for stories, spending some time thinking about what is going to happen and what his characters might say.

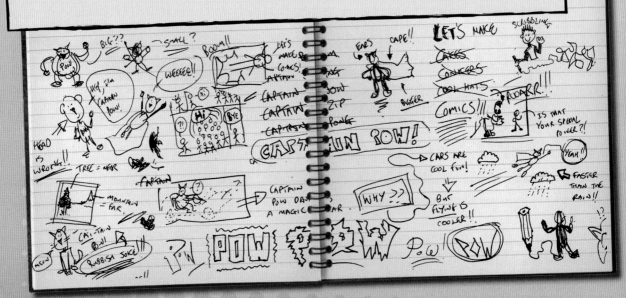

Robin's scribbling secrets

1. Think of an interesting beginning!

> Honey-stealing aliens come to Earth.

We come in hunger! Give us your honey!

2. Fill the middle with action!

> Captain Pow arrives with his bee friends.

Beehave, aliens! Or my friends will *bee* angry!

3. Try to end with a surprise!

Agh! We're allergic to bees! We thought honey came from trees.

> The Aliens flee Earth in fear.

Next we're going to need some **panels** ...

CHAPTER 6:
PANELS

Once you've got an idea for a story and some characters, it's time to add the panels!

Comic panels work a bit like a picture frame. They hold the action in place ...

... and they stop characters from falling out of the comic!

Panels can be different shapes ...

... but square or rectangular panels are the most common.

Hey! I'm not common!

Or square!

Let's put our honey-stealing alien story into three panels and see what it looks like.

You can now see that the first panel will need to be a little bit bigger to fit in the spaceship. Try to leave room for important background details.

Flip for bubble trouble ...

CHAPTER 7:
BUBBLES AND WORDS

Whenever a character talks in your comic, you must draw a **speech bubble** above their head to hold all the words in place.

Different shaped bubbles have different uses. Which speech bubble on the right matches the descriptions here?

- Spiky bubbles are used when characters are shouting.
- A circular bubble is used when characters are talking normally.
- A fluffy cloud-shaped bubble is used when characters are thinking.

BONUS BOX!
A rectangular box is used to describe what's happening in the picture. This is not a speech bubble but it's very useful!

CHAPTER 8:
SOUND EFFECTS

It's not just characters that use words – comics are really noisy!

From balloons popping ...   ... to glass breaking.

 **POP!**  **CRACK!**

From computer games ...   ... to real games.

 **ZAP!**    **BOOT!**

If something makes a noise in real life, it can make a noise in your story. These words are called **sound effects**.

YOUR TURN! Take a good look at this runaway monster.
What sound effects would you add to this action-packed picture?

Sound effects give your comic an extra layer of
excitement. Plus, they are great fun to create!

Turn for
added details!

CHAPTER 9:
DETAILS

Does your story have a beginning, middle and an end? Is it clear what your stick people are doing in the pictures? Yes? Then you've made a great comic!

But there's more fun to be had!

Making comic books is a bit like building your very own imaginary world. You can add as much detail as you want.

ART TIP

Try adding detail to your characters by using simple shapes, such as the dog below.

With a little practice,
your trees will *bloom* ...

... and your cars will *zoom!*

Your castles will *soar* ...

... and your lions will *roar!*

And adding colour to your pictures will really help
your comics come alive before your very eyes!

You did it ...

CHAPTER 10:
YOU DID IT!

You are now safely on your way to making your very first comic. This is a great day!

BUT NOW WHAT?
Once you've finished your comic, your friends and family (and pet robot) can read it!

- What was their favourite story moment?
- What was their favourite panel?
- Who was their favourite character?

Hooray! Congratulations! Well done! Let's party!

You can create any comic story you like, using:
- ideas and genres
- characters and panels
- bubbles and words
- sound effects and details.

So, are you ready for your next adventure? Grab your paper and pencils, jump back to Chapter 1 and ...

LET'S MAKE A NEW COMIC!

GLOSSARY

characters: the people in a story, film or comic
genre: a type of story, e.g. adventure, romance
panels: the frames around the drawings in a comic
sound effects: words to show a sound in a comic, e.g. CRASH!
speech bubble: a shape containing words that a character is saying

INDEX